MY ANC
WAS A
POLICEMAN

HOW CAN I FIND OUT MORE ABOUT HIM?

by
Antony Shearman

SOCIETY OF GENEALOGISTS
2000

Published by
Society of Genealogists Enterprises Limited
14 Charterhouse Buildings
Goswell Road
London EC1M 7BA

© Antony Shearman 2000
Reprinted 2007

ISBN 10: 1 903462 00 2
ISBN 13: 978 1 903462 00 3

British Library Cataloguing in Publication Data
A CIP Catalogue record for this book is available from the British Library

Society of Genealogists Enterprises Limited is a wholly owned subsidiary of
Society of Genealogists, a registered charity, no 233701

INTRODUCTION

This booklet contains details of some 250 archives with references to many thousands of names recorded in the police force registers in Britain. Since the act of 1829 the force has grown steadily in number. An appreciable number of these records are held on closed access but are listed so that the time of the researcher need not be wasted in looking for records which cannot be seen.

Since the original research was carried out it is possible that records have been transferred from police authority to the local record office.

In addition police museums have been set up (or are intended to be) and records are held there against expansion plans.

It is suggested that this booklet is used in conjunction with *Record Repositories in Great Britain,* ed. Ian Mortimer.

ACKNOWLEDGEMENTS

My thanks are due to the many people in the police force, in record offices and in police museums who have provided information and details of holdings.

Help from the staff at the Royal Commission on Historical Manuscripts was much appreciated, especially the provision of the basic record which they photocopied from the subject index of the National Register of Archives.

In particular Alan Hayhurst for the Police History Society was supportive from the start. Colin Jackson and Michael Torr were instrumental in disentangling most of the intricacies of Yorkshire and in supplying the list of records available. Similarly Michael Smith traced items which contributed to filling previous omissions in Cheshire.

My family have been actively involved in the work including some difficult keyboarding and proof reading. Any omissions or errors must, however, be laid at my door. I should be grateful to receive information concerning any significant collections of police personnel records which can be made available to family historians. Finally my thanks to John Titford for his wholehearted support and enthusiasm.

Antony Shearman

ILLUSTRATIONS

Greater Manchester Police Museum have allowed reproduction of three photographs showing the development of uniforms and 'technology'. The cover cartoon is reproduced by permission of Punch Ltd.

CONTENTS

A SHORT HISTORY OF THE POLICE FORCE IN BRITAIN

The first use of the noun 'policeman' is shown in the *Shorter Oxford English Dictionary* as dating from 1829. This was the year that the Act of Parliament for improving the police was introduced by Sir Robert Peel. The word 'police' had a far longer use and with much the same meaning as we know today: '*Politia*' (Medieval Latin), '*police*' (French), and '*Pollis*' in Scotland and Ireland (as it is still pronounced there). In 1716 as a verb, it signified the 'regulation, control and discipline of a community, enforcement of the Law and public order'.

The Duke of Wellington, Prime Minister in 1829 gave his view that the police in London were an entire success: 'It is impossible,' he said, 'to see anything more respectable than they are'.

The Royal Irish Constabulary was legally constituted in 1836, covering all Ireland apart from the Dublin Metropolitan Police Force, formed in 1786.

The Marine Police was instituted about 1798 to protect merchant shipping on the Thames in the Port of London.

The Railway Police began operating in 1837, but it should be noted that railwaymen refer to a signalman as a policeman. From 1963 the British Transport Police covered railways in England, Scotland and Wales, and included the London Underground system and now the Docklands Light Railway.

Women police patrols were appointed in February 1919 but without being sworn in as constables with power of arrest, until April 1923. Records of Service have not apparently survived from that period.

WAS YOUR ANCESTOR A PARISH CONSTABLE?

Constables operated to preserve the peace within a parish or township (civil division of a parish). The position evolved from the chief officer of a royal fortress or castle to a local representative assisted by a watchman. Originally his duties were bound up with the regulation of the manorial court. In 1381 the office of Justice of the Peace was established. The constable had to report to him and to take action on a wide range of occurrences such as 'felonies committed, escaped prisoners, riots, and unlawful assemblies, non-attendance at church, oppression by other officers, commercial irregularities, licensing of ale houses, compiling jurors' lists, drunkenness, unauthorized building of additional cottages and dovecotes, vagabonds, intruders, militia muster rolls, taking lewd women before the Justice of the Peace, and detaining refractory fathers of bastards'. Terrick Fitzhugh, *Dictionary of Genealogy*.

It may be helpful to see how this formidable array of duties translated on the ground. One of my ancestors was churchwarden and overseer of the poor in a small Huntingdonshire village in the mid eighteenth century. He worked closely with the constable. By good fortune their accounts have survived and it is possible to have a glimpse of how these posts were financed and what expenses they incurred:

'1752 The disbursements of Thomas Wakling, Overseer of ye ways. Dew (*due*) to the Town £3.2s.6d; a Journey and sworn (*swearing?*) 3s.0d; paid for a warrant. 2s.6d; paid for young cubs (*presumably vermin*) 6d; paid for (*a*)ssessing the Tax at Alconbury; 1s.6d for going to the Sessions at ditto 1s.6d; Going to Kimbolton Sessions 2s.0d; given to two sailors 6d; a man with a pass 6d; Paid to Mr Thong for the Highways, inditing & charge £2.7s.6d.

'1757 1d in the pound levy upon the account of the Militia. A levy made by the consent of the parishioners of Buckworth to Jno Hunt, Constable at a half penny in the pound for the year.

'1759 (*contributors*) : Mr Nickolls £261.10s.10d; Jno Hunt £122.5s.1d; Thomas Waklin £87.3s.7d; Mr Case £66.2s.9d; Mr Ball £23.0s.11d; Jno Sharman £20.0s.10d; Widow Sterne £8.0s.4d.' Huntingdonshire County Record Office: *Rev. Sutton's Survey* (ref PPPP 830).

Constables were unpaid, and often reluctant, and they did not need a property qualification until 1842 when they had to occupy land assessed to the poor or county rate of at least £4.0s.0d a year. A Wiltshire Constable sums up the disrepute into which the post had fallen: 'I am unlearned and by reason thereof am constrayned to go two miles from my house to have the help of a scrivener to read such warrants as are sent to me.' (*Source not known*).

HENRY FIELDING AND THE BOW STREET RUNNERS

In the towns and cities, parochial constables were assisted by watchmen and were responsible to the Justices of the Peace. Henry Fielding (1707-1754), novelist, dramatist and barrister, became chairman of quarter sessions at Hicks Hall in 1749. Today he is best known as the author of Tom Jones, which graphically portrayed the lawlessness in the capital city. He attacked social ills, especially gin drinking, and carried out an *Inquiry into the increase of Robbers in London.* He was made a Justice of the Peace and with his half brother set up the Bow Street Runners. In 1753 he propounded an elaborate scheme for the building of county workhouses. The same year Fielding set up a system of paid informers against robber gangs by creating a special fund, and succeeded in breaking up a notorious gang.

Sir John Fielding (died 1780) was a half brother of Henry and a magistrate in his own right, though apparently blind from birth. He carried on the plan for breaking up the robber gangs and originated a scheme for sending 'distressed' boys into the Royal Navy and a similar plan for rescuing deserted girls (1758). The Bow Street Runners (1750) were an embryo detective force employing paid constables in London. Fielding's recommendations led to the setting up of further police offices, each with a magistrate who was in charge of clerks and constables. These last were in addition to the London Parish constables. They wore red waistcoats and were often called 'Robin Redbreasts'. They were never more than about eight or ten in number. After Fielding died, in 1754, the Runners became corrupted. They mixed with criminals and when there was a theft or burglary, they soon found out who had committed the crime. Then, promising not to arrest or charge the thieves, the Runners arranged with them to return some of the stolen goods. In this way they received payment from both the owners of the stolen property, and also from the thieves. Some of the runners were found to be very rich when they died.

The Bow Street Horse Patrol was incorporated into the Metropolitan Force in 1836 and operated in outlying Divisions.

ACT FOR IMPROVING THE POLICE IN AND NEAR THE METROPOLIS (1829)

Between Fielding's Bow Street Runners and Sir Robert Peel's Act of 1829, national and international events gave an increased impetus to the need for reform of the forces of law and order. The American Revolution (1776) and the French Revolution (1789) had the effect of de-stabilizing the population and highway robbery was at its height.

A symptom of this, was the increased social and industrial unrest, leading to the Gordon Riots 1780, the Luddites about 1812, and the Peterloo Massacre 1819. The only response available to the government was to raise a military force. In 1812 an army of 12,000 men was deployed in the North and the Midlands in an effort to suppress the machine wrecking Luddites, rioting against low wages and unemployment.

Ten years later, in 1822, a select committee report on the police in the Metropolis warned of restrictions being made on civil liberties, however desirable the ends. This caution held up reform for a further seven years. Sir Robert Peel's Act was passed in 1829 and the first police commissioners were appointed – these being a lawyer, Richard Mayne, and a soldier, Charles Rowan.

Although the police force was to be a civil authority, the influence of Charles Rowan, an army colonel who had fought and been wounded at Waterloo, can be detected in the army-style discipline and routines which have persisted over 150 years. Recruitment was originally from the army and navy for the senior ranks.

The first policemen appeared on the streets of London on the evening of Tuesday, 29 September 1829, and were known as Metropolitan or 'New' police. They wore tailcoats and top hats and carried wooden batons or sticks under their coat tails. These were the policemen we know today, although the tail coat became a jacket, and in 1864 the top hat was replaced by a helmet. The policeman was required to be aged under 35, be at least 5' 7" tall, be literate and of good character.

Initially people treated the new police with great hostility. Constables on the beat were greeted with various abusive names such as 'Peelers' (after Sir Robert Peel), 'Blue Devils' or 'Raw Lobsters'. In some dangerous areas, constables were stabbed to death. Later, with names such as 'Bobby' (from Sir Robert) and 'Copper' for one who captures or arrests, they came to be regarded almost with affection.

By the end of the nineteenth century, the country had almost complete police coverage.

As an example of the duties of a country policeman and to demonstrate the value, genealogically, of examination books, the following from Berkshire Constabulary may serve to show the further evolution of police work:

'PC71, aged 31 at date of application; height: 5' 8"; visage: thin; complexion: pale; eyes: hazel; hair: fair; particular marks: none; figure: slender; where born? (*answer:*) in the parish of St. Margarets, Westminster, Middlesex; trade or calling? (*answer:*) none; read and write? (*answer:*) both; single or married? (*answer:*) single; residence? (*answer:*) London; what public service? (*answer:*) Army and Police; regiment or corps etc.? (*answer:*) 83rd Regiment and Metropolitan Police; length of service? (*answer:*) 10 years. When discharged and with whom last employed? Approved and sworn (*signed*) Surgeons Certificate: verified fit for the constabulary of this County. Date of appointment'.

After six years PC71 was promoted from second class PC to first class PC, and after a further eight years, to Merit Class PC. In all he served 26 years: 'date of removal from the Force? amount of superannuation? (*answer:*) 18*s.*3*d* per week'. His lack of promotion for one who could read and write is perhaps explained in part by the remarks which follow, written in red ink:

'1866 Fined 7/6 for neglect of duty in not reporting a case of moving Cattle.

'1875: Granted one penny per diem – good conduct pay.

'1881: Pay reduced from 27/5 to 26/3 per week for using improper language when at the execution of his duty.

'1888: pay restored to 27/5 per week

'1889: Fined 5/- for omitting to report a serious crime to his Supt. for three days after he had heard of it himself.

'1890: Fined 5/- for not meeting his Sergt. at a conference point.'

P.C. 71 lived until 1927, dying at the age of 93.
Source: Examination book held at Berkshire County Record Office.

Due to population movement from the countryside to towns and cities, police effort was mainly required in urban rather than rural areas. The consequence was the setting up of borough and city police forces which took place with surprising speed so that by the end of the nineteenth century most populated parts of Britain were covered. County police forces contributed to this coverage so that many records which have survived date from the 1860s as Mr Waters explains below.

Forces ranged in size from Manchester, Leeds and Lancashire to Rutland and the Liberty of Peterborough which had the smallest establishment in the country at just eleven men. These variations in size led to rationalisation and amalgamations designed to even out the cost of the police force.

TYPES OF RECORD

Borough Police

Register of officers and constables

Discipline books – invaluable, as they are likely to contain personal information such as date of joining, (physical) description, pay, promotions, awards, misconduct, date of leaving and pension.

Other records less likely to provide personal information about a single officer are the general Order Book, Occurrence Book, Charge Book, Chief Constable's Annual Report, Watch Committee Minutes and a published history of the borough force.

County Police

Attestation papers showing a brief description (physical), age, birth place, trade, date appointed, postings and date of leaving the force.

Personal files, if they survive are available for research.

Less likely sources are general orders, survival of records and the Chief Constable's Annual Report. The force magazine/newspaper can contain promotion details, retirements and obituaries.

Pension books if available can be useful for dates and length of service.

Photographs showing changes in uniform from stove-pipe hat and frock coat to open neck tunic with shirt and tie can be difficult to date precisely except by an expert.

SURVIVAL OF RECORDS

'This is a real problem for the family historian. Generally speaking police records have only survived in a piecemeal fashion. Most modern police forces date from before 1860 and their first buildings date from this era. These original buildings have long since been demolished, or ceased to be police buildings, as forces have grown or up-dated their accommodation. Similarly police forces have been subject to one or more amalgamations and these again proved to be occasions when the old was deliberately swept away and replacement organisations tried to establish new identities. In addition the paper pulping demands of two world wars took their toll. Police officers have been reluctant to hand over their records for preservation by other agencies. Only the Metropolitan Police are covered by the provisions of the Public Records Act 1958. There is currently considerable pressure on Chief Constables to continually improve effectiveness and efficiency, and this climate is not conducive to devoting scarce resources to establish police archives. The net effect is that it may be safest in the first instance for the family historian to assume that a record has not survived. Some records do however have a slightly higher chance of survival than others. Old personnel and discipline books have often survived as they have always been seen to be highly confidential and valuable. With the above exceptions other survivals are of a chance nature. Indeed some survivals have come about because of the curiosity of individual officers who have saved some book from destruction to keep it and return to a force museum many years later. On other occasions in the distant past old records have no doubt been 'borrowed' by collectors, never to be seen again'. Taken from *Notes for Family Historians*. L.A. Waters, Police History Society.

BRITISH POLICE FORCE RECORDS: GAZETTEER AND DIRECTORY OF SOURCES

Reference Numbers

The following directory of sources lists archives recorded in the subject index of the National Register of Archives (NRA) held at the Royal Commission on Historical Manuscripts at Quality house, Quality Court, Chancery Lane, London WC2A 1HP. The RCHM staff also maintain ARCHON which acts as a gateway to Internet resources for British archivists or researchers at http://www.hmc.gov.uk.

The National Register of Archives (Scotland) NRA(S) is maintained by the Scottish Record Office (code 234) at HM General Register House, Edinburgh, EH1 3YY.

Four or five figure numbers preceded by the letters NRA or NRA(S) indicate police records mentioned on the subject index of the National Register of Archives. These entries have been checked for the presence of personnel records and in some cases the absence of such records has been noted. Individual policemen have not been included.

Entries in the NRA relate to record office or private holdings and often show a document reference number, for example HDX 1577.

Record office addresses have been identified by a code number taken from *Record Repositories in Great Britain* edited by Ian Mortimer and published by PRO Publications. If you have access to a computer these codes may be used in conjunction with ARCHON. Researchers are advised to consult this useful booklet or subsequent edition for current details and addresses.

Entries added to the NRA are extracted from annual reports and notifications to the staff at Quality Court. Such entries have a reference number and year, for example 1991, DD/2/1.

The main alternative source of police archive details is in *Guide to sources for police history,* Police History Society, edited by Ian Bridgeman and Clive Emsley. This is out of print and police authority holdings may have been transferred to a local record office or police museum archive. Where an entry does not carry a reference or NRA number, the indication is that the archive is retained in the possession of the police authority concerned. In some instances this may result in closed access for a period up to 100 years or more. A letter addressed to the Curator at police HQ with a stamped addressed envelope is worth trying in this instance. Current addresses can be found in local phone books. Police museums are coded (M) or (MS = collection in store).

Within each entry the sequence is mostly: PLACE in bold, TYPE of force e.g. constabulary, YEARS covered by each record, the record itself, LOCATION (where held), and REFERENCE numbers.

Aberdeen *see* Grampian Police

Airdrie District Police Commissioners
    Glasgow City Archives (code 243) Lanarkshire CC (C01/10/9/1-2) 1846-90
    cash book 1846-81
    general ledger 1846-90

Anglesey County Constabulary, now North Wales police, HQ Glan-y-don, Clwyd, LL29. Some records held at Anglesey County Record Office, (code 221), including Holyhead, and Menai Bridge 1867-1955
    Station records 1912-1930, photographs and artefacts. Anglesey Police (WH and WM 1779)

Angus County Constabulary: 1927-62
    Enquiries to the Hon. Curator, Tayside Police Museum, Police Headquarters PO Box 59, West Bell Street, Dundee DD1 9JU. (code 618) (M). Papers relating to Police Authorities are now incorporated with Tayside Region Police
    pay receipts 1854 at Forfarshire County Constabulary
    Perthshire and Kinross-shire Constabulary 1857-about 1936
    Railway Constabulary pay book 1848-1961
    Dundee Burgh Police 1851-about 1974
    Women's auxiliary police corps 1941-48
    Montrose Burgh Police book 1865-1921: (photographs including officers on duty, on parade, on special occasions; police pipe bands and sportsmen)
    presentation of medals about 1884-1984
    Perth City Police: magazine notes on various topics e.g. police women

Arundel Borough Police: Feb 1836-Apr 1889
    West Sussex Record Office (code 182)
    Station records; Aug 1876-Jul 1880
    duty book recording day, date, name and rank of police officers, time of going on and off duty, state of the weather and remarks (ref POL AB)

Ashton under Lyne Borough Police
Lancashire Record Office (code 55)
examination book 1848-1940
discipline book 1931-47

Avon and Somerset Constabulary: HQ PO Box 37 Valley Road, Portishead Bristol BS20 8QJ. 1856-1980
Somerset Archive and Record Service (code 168)
records mainly of former Somerset and Bath City Constabulary (ref DD/ASC) also most of the former Avon County Council records. Includes personnel records
1935-41 reservists
1970-73 discipline and dismissals
1920-44 discipline reports, Bristol. Nine volumes
1936-64 residence-addresses
1941-65 medical reports
1946-54 applications, recruits
1946-48 retirements
1960 joining register – pensions, Bristol 1864-1948
special constables about 1940
admin personnel records 1945-55

Bacup Borough Police
Lancashire Record Office (code 55)
personnel record book 1887-1938
registers of constables 1887-1946

Bamber Bridge Lancashire Constabulary: 1937-50
Lancashire Record Office (code 55)
Special Constabulary record cards (ref PLA acc 6041). These are subject to fifty years closure

Barnsley Police Force
Barnsley Archive and Local Studies Dept (code 196)
pay books 1896-1961
file of personnel sheets 1935-54 – alphabetical list of name, date of joining includes some genealogical details, such as date and place of origin, and sometimes information about parents; examination of candidates for force – gives name, age, address, place of birth, trade and last employer (ref 547/C)
Restricted access applies, permission must be obtained from South Yorkshire Police Community Affairs Dept or Sheffield Archives (code 199)

Barrow in Furness Borough Police
Cumbria record office (code 25)
registers of constables 1881-1920

Bath *see* **Avon and Somerset**

Bedfordshire Constabulary
Bedfordshire and Luton Archives and Record Service (code 4)
force conduct book 1927-40 (M)

Berkshire Constabulary
Berkshire County Record Office until 2000 (code 5)
police examination book and detailed index 1856-1929
medical examination books 1938-57. These are closed until 1998-2001

Birkenhead Borough Police
Cheshire Record Office (code 17) ref CJP 20/6/11-16
wages books 1870-1943
records and pensions 1886-1921
1947 pension register (with police authority)

Birmingham Special Constabulary: see also West Midlands Police 1939-42
Birmingham City Archives. Birmingham Reference Library (code 143) (misc MS659)
E. Division, Coventry Road Police Station; notebooks of policemen

Blackburn Borough Police Force
Lancashire Record Office (code 55) (ref PLA acc 6401)
personnel record sheets about 1910-1960s
register of candidates about 1919-44
service register (ref PLA55/4-6) about 1946-67
register of discharge certificate stubs (ref PLA55/4-6)
register of candidates about 1928-44
service register about 1946-67
Blackburn Library:
personnel record sheets about 1854-1907
declarations registers 1911-38
war reserve register 1914-17
discharge certificate stubs about 1920-46

Blackpool Borough Police Force
Lancashire Record Office (code 55)
examination book (ref PLB 5/1) 1887-1919

Training Bolton Borough Police in morse code in the 1930s

presentation volume of photographs of policemen 1906 (PLA acc 6428)
correspondence concerning medals awarded to policemen (PLA acc 6415) 1916-77
There is a 30 year closure

Blaenau Ffestiniog and **Penrhyndeudraeth** Police Area
Gwynedd, Merioneth Archives, Area Record office (code 220)
occurrence books and order books 1855-1986

Bolton see **Manchester Greater**

Boston Borough Police
Register of constables held by police authority 1856-1927

Bradford City Police
West Yorkshire Archive Service, Wakefield (code 201)
register of officers and constables (indexed) (ref A124/138) 1918-49
examination books 1897-1911 (A259/1-2)
disciplinary book 1883-96 (A250/3)
defaulters books 1859-98, 1918-49 (A250/4)
applications for appointments by constables 1920-60 (A295/2)
ex-police personnel files 1940-73 (A295/3)
These records are subject to a 40-year time limit

Brentford constable: Brentford, Middlesex
Hounslow Public Libraries, Brentford District Library (Hounslow misc 17785)
accounts 1688-1710

British Transport Police: see also PRO Source sheet no 13
letters, applications and testimonials: GW Railway Police 1869
Midland Railway personnel 1897-1920.
Nottingham station 1910-46

Bristol *see* **Avon and Somerset**

Buckinghamshire *see* **Thames Valley**

Burnley Borough Police Force
Lancashire Record Office (code 55)
constables' application forms 1887-1921 (ref PLA 5471)
pay receipt book and pay rolls; 1892-1951 (incomplete series) (PLA/3/1-8, 4/1-7)
testimonials for application to the Force 1887 (PLA acc 6451)

Bury *see* **Lancashire**

Caernarvonshire Constabulary

Caernarfon area record office: ref Caerns Constabulary (code 219) (XJ, XS/1234) records of staffing, nominal rolls, testimonials and applications 1857 – twentieth century papers ref Wynn (XD2/14108-218) 1856-79

Caithness County Constabulary

Highland Council Archive (code 232) miscellaneous personnel files of former members of joint forces and civilian employees. Contains details of appointment, pay, pensions, deductions, training, reports and other correspondence (no dates given)

Cambridge Borough

discipline book 1921-64 register of pensioners, (no date)

Cambridgeshire Constabulary

Cambridgeshire County Police authority (M) discipline book 1921-40

Cardiff Borough Police

Glamorgan Archives Service (code 214) 1841-1971 crime registers, inquest records, journals, occurrences books and personnel records 1862-1907 (ref Cardiff Police D/D Con/C). NOTE: permission must be sought in writing in advance of visit from the South Wales Police Museum *see* **South Wales**

Chard United Police

Somerset Archive and record service (code 214) minutes, receipt and payment book, accounts 1849-57, ref Somerset Archaeological Society (DD/SAS (C/909/911). Includes a petition to help immigrants to Australia

Cheshire County Police Force

Cheshire Record Office (code 17) enrolment and record books 1857-1913 (ref CJP 20/2/1) register of appointments 1923-66 (CJP 24/1) register of married officers 1847-1960 (CJF/2) Cheshire Special Constabulary (ref DDX 489) Stockton Heath and Walton Special Constables' records list of persons serving 1940-44

Chester City Police:
Cheshire Record Office (code 17)
roll of members 1836-1939 (ref CJP 20/7/1)

Chesterfield, Derbyshire County Constabulary
Derbyshire County Record Office (code 26)
county constabulary candidates' joining register 1859-1921
personnel register 1913-1946

City of Glasgow Police *see* **Glasgow City Archives**

City of London *see* **London, City of**

Cleveland Constabulary *see* **Teeside**

Clitheroe Borough Police Force
Lancashire Record Office (code 55)
list of past and present officers from *Clitheroe Borough Record* 1947 (ref PLA acc 6481)

Congleton Borough Police
Cheshire Record Office (code 17)
registers 1926-50 (ref CJP 17/6-7)

Cornwall *see* **Devon and Cornwall Constabulary**

Coventry Police Force
Coventry City Archives (code 144) (ref Coventry Police CC/PO)
annual reports, wages books, daily order books etc. 1836-1970

Derby Borough Police
records held at Derbyshire County Record office (code 26) 1836-1947

Derbyshire County Constabulary
Derbyshire Record Office (code 26) ref (D3376) Guide 1992
personnel 1857-1914
discipline report book 1921-25
personal descriptive register and photographs (M)
See also **Glossop, Chesterfield** and **Derby** Borough Police

Devon and Cornwall Constabulary
Devon Record Office (code 27) (M)
candidates rejected list 1885-1941
miscellaneous records and personnel files 1929-81 (ref 4107 M add 12)

complaint book Plympton Division 6 August 1964 – 14 April 1975 (G)
NOTE: this file is closed until 2096. Until 60 years after the last date in each volume, public access to and inspection of these volumes is at the discretion of the archivist who will treat each request for research access on its merits, bearing in mind the personal nature of the material in these volumes and the nature and scope of the research subject. Where access is granted under this provision, it may be subject to such controls and conditions as the archivist thinks fit.

Dewsbury Borough Police
West Yorkshire Archive Service (code 201)
ex-police personnel files 1940-73 (ref A295/5)
NOTE: subject to a 40 year time limit

Doncaster Police
Sheffield Archives (code 199) (ref 296/C)
record and defaulters' book, indexed 1886-1931
photographs 1926-41
wages books 1890-1951

Dorset Constabulary
Dorset Police (ref D315) (MS)
personnel registers 1871-1947
Other records are at Dorset Record Office (code 31)

Dudley *see* **West Midlands**

Dundee Police
Dundee City Archives (code 251) (ref Dundee misc GD/x19/9)
(War time) Special Constable reserve 1939-46
muster and nominal rolls of personnel (two files, two notebooks in one volume)
See also **Angus**

Durham Police
Durham County Record Office (code 32)
index to Chief Constables' reports 1883-1958 (ref CCP/5)
personnel register 1885 (ref CCP/0)

East Lothian Police
Edinburgh City Archives (code 236)
personnel records 1878-1954: Edinburgh 1920-68
Establishment Book, list of Force and conditions, also known as the Edinburgh Police Register 1815-59

East Riding, Yorkshire *see* **Humberside**

East Suffolk Constabulary: 1890-95
Police authority: list of payments into the coffee fund – two volumes 1895-57

Edinburgh City Police
Edinburgh City Archives (code 236) (ref Lothian Police ED/006/13)
personnel records in twenty two volumes 1887-1964
returns of crime January 1847
lists of sergeants and constables, August 1848

Essex County Constabulary
Essex Record Office (code 37)
general force registers 1840-1910 giving name, age, date of birth, height, trade, marital status, date of removal and reasons (ref J/P 2/1-2)
promotion registers giving name, rank, dates of joining, appointment, date of removal and reasons 1840-90, 1939-48 (ref J/P 2/1-2)
distribution of Force returns giving name, rank and number of officers at each station, dates of joining Force and station 1888-1951 (J/P1-31)
See also **Southend**

Forfarshire *see* **Angus**

Garstang and Rossendale Division, Lancashire Constabulary
Lancashire Record Office (code 55)
constables' joining books 1881-1966 (ref PLA acc 5537)

Glamorgan Constabulary
Glamorgan Archive Service, (code 214) (ref Glamorgan Const. DD Con 280-300)
records include district and divisional testimonials, swearing in books 1841-1969
register about 1890 and 1937-39
list of pensioners; thirty notebooks kept by PCs, poems and cards 1849-1943
See also **South Wales**

Glasgow
Glasgow City Archives (code 243)
registers of Constabulary 1857 – date

Glossop Borough Police (Derbyshire)
Derbyshire Record Office (code 26)
staff record 1901-39

Gloucestershire Constabulary

no historical records: enquiries directed to Gloucestershire Record Office (code 40)

Holdings include recruitment and service records, photographs, station diaries, discipline report book (1933-52) and financial records

Murder enquiry papers form the basis of existing records (for training purposes) (ref Glos Constabulary Q/Y) (M)

Gloucestershire Record Office (Glos RO misc D5184) (code 40)

notebooks of Chief Superintendent Harry Thomas, formerly secretary of the National Association of Retired Police Officers 1937, 1955-59

register of members 1970-76

Grampian Police

HQ, Queen Street, Aberdeen. AB9 1BA. Museum being constructed

Apply to The Curator, Force Welfare Office at the above address

Greater Manchester *see* **Manchester, Greater**

Great Yarmouth

Police Authority personnel record 1871-1974

Griffithstown police station, Monmouthshire

Gwent Record office (code 218)

records including 100 PCs' journals and information books 1908-35 (ref D2113)

Grimsby Borough Police

North East Lincolnshire Archives (code 48) miscellaneous records 1871-99 (X 50)

No personnel records listed in NE Lincs

Guernsey, States of

personnel files retained by the Island Police

Halifax Police Joint Branch Board

West Yorkshire Archive Service, Calderdale (code 203) (ref Calderdale misc MISC 5/97)

miscellaneous records 1919-68 (ref D2113)

register of force 1872-1967

Hampshire Constabulary

Hampshire Record Office (code 41)

general orders, constables' reports, personnel records, licensing records, station reports and messages book 1840-1967

Examination books 1840-1967 (ref 200M86) on microfiche, closed from 1924 for seventy years
press cuttings and scrapbook 1884-1964 opened in 1995
constables' declaration 1899-1933 (ref 200M86 H12/1-4)
promotion register (200M86, H14, H16)
See also **Portsmouth, Southampton, Winchester**

Herefordshire Constabulary
Hereford Record Office (code 44) (ref Hereford misc AH 35)
daily state of constables 1906-19, 1921-61 (closed from 1961 for 100 years)

Hertfordshire Constabulary
Police authority
candidates register 1931-41
clothing register 1926-45

Holyhead *see* **Anglesey**

Horncastle Lighting and Watching Inspectors
Lincolnshire Archives: Tweed Solicitors (code 57) (3TP/1)
records 1838-67, (e.g. correspondence concerning Isaac Slade, temporarily sent to Horncastle by the Metropolitan Police to deal with an outbreak of robberies, 1845)

Huddersfield Borough Constabulary
West Yorkshire Archive Service, Wakefield (code 201)
constables' record books 1891-1957 (ref A147/4-5)
personnel 1860-1918 (ref. A83/72)

Hull City Police
East Riding of Yorkshire Record Office (code 47)
personnel register 1860-1919
rewards and commendations register 1860-1920

Humberside Police Authority
East Riding of Yorkshire Archives Office (code 47) (1994 Acc. 2824)
ex members personnel files, roll books 1893-1974
predecessor files; records from training centre 1836-1980

Huntingdonshire now Cambridgeshire Constabulary
Cambridgeshire County Record Office (code 11)
personnel register, Huntingdon 1857-1936
special courts; individual and group photographs from various dates 1930-70

commendations 1928-63

discipline book 1938-69 (cover says Leightonstone, but is actually for the whole county)

NOTE: there may be a closure date set on more recent records

Inverness-shire Constabulary

Highland County Archive (code 232)

personal record book 1838-82

candidates' appointment books 1891-1969

register of police pensions and gratuities 1882-1958

record and defaulters books (covers officers appointed between 1911 and 1937 with records of their service up to 1958)

service records 1936-68

NOTE: there is a closure period on personnel records of 100 years

Isle of Man Constabulary

Manx National Heritage Library (code 147)

register of Officers and Constables 1874-1945

NOTE: there is a hundred year embargo period on these records. However, library staff are allowed to extract information about constables or officers who served prior to 1898, and provide details of their service in response to postal enquirers

Isle of Wight

Isle of Wight County Record Office (code 189)

register of constables 1890-1941 including index. NOTE: Closed for 70 years

Jersey, States of

A new archive centre is to open to the public in 2000 but personnel records not available

Kent Constabulary

personnel records and index 1833-86

personnel records of service 1857-1939

candidates 1857-1939

resignations 1875-99

Kent Police Museum: Chatham Historic Dockyard

For Police family history enquiries write to the Curator who undertakes police ancestry research at the Centre for Kentish Studies (code 51) (M)

Kinross-shire *see* Angus

Kirkham Division, Lancashire Constabulary
Lancashire Record Office (code 55)
constables' joining books 1865-1959 (ref PLA acc 5733)
list of special constables 1938-47 (ref DDX 1290 acc 4365)

Lancashire Constabulary: 1939-48: Bury Division 1926-45: Radcliffe Special
Lancashire Record Office (code 55) (ref DDX 1521)
NOTE: although the public cannot look at examination books less than one hundred
years old, nor any of the personnel record sheets, staff are allowed to consult both
sources, extract information about a constable who joined before 1949, and send it
by post. A fee is payable for this service (unless the searcher can state the policeman's
collar number or year of joining). General closure periods: 30 years, but most
personnel records (other than above) closed for 50 years
reports, correspondence, registers etc 1845-1989
index to examination books 1925-86
personnel file for those retired in 1986
Also a summary list of personnel records with dates of operation of each force
Service Registers, personnel record sheets and photographs 1900-68 (ref PLA 54)
Seniority register 1939-68, closed until 1999; lists of personnel grouped by rank,
and date of joining, date of birth, and a small amount of other information
Special Constabulary Service register with index: closed until 2069 (ref PLA 19) (M)
See also **Ashton under Lyne, Bacup, Bamber Bridge, Barrow in Furness,
Blackburn, Blackpool, Burnley, Clitheroe, Garstang and Rossendale, Kirkham,
Little Lever, Preston, Radcliffe, Rochdale, Southport** and **Wigan**
Also available is a summary list of personnel records and where to find them with
dates of operation of each force

Leeds City Police 'A' Division
West Yorkshire Archive Service, Wakefield (code 201)
personnel register 1900-51 ref (A90/196); East Division 1946-71 (ref A238/40)
joiners 1835-1935 (ref A137/254)
Roll of Honour 1833-1920 (ref A72/164 HQ 3370)
conduct books – 18 volumes with index (ref A83 105-9, HQ 4246; A137,
253-264 HQ 9000-9009)
Force members (incomplete) 1920-49 (ref A299/44/49)
resignations 1912-67 (ref 137/165)
applications for appointments by constables 1910-60 (ref 295/15)

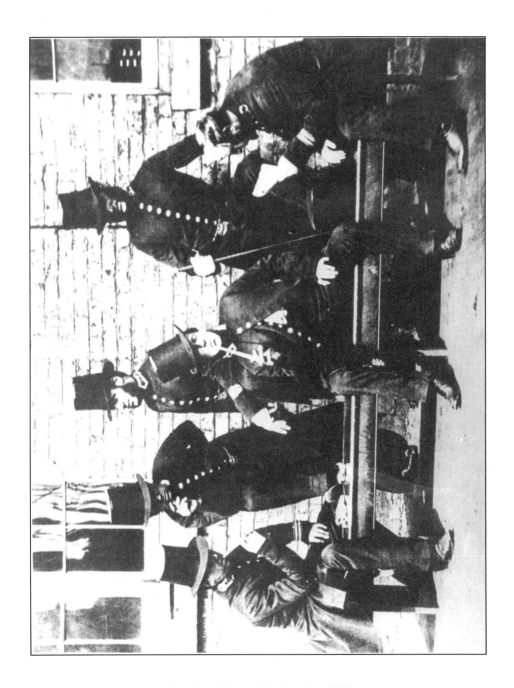

Manchester Borough Police about 1850

Leicester City Police
Leicestershire Record Office (code 56)
station journals, crime, licensing and personnel records 1853-1958
certificates of discharge 1909-67 (DE 3831)

Leicestershire Constabulary
minutes, personnel 1839-76, (including a register of force)
pensions 1857-1959
personal records 1922-54
NOTE: for further police records, apply to County Council, Leicester Corporation
See also quarter sessions records in the Leicestershire Collection (MS)

Liberty of Peterborough *see* **Peterborough**

Lincoln Police: register held by Police Authority 1857-1901

Lincolnshire
The Curator, Police HQ, PO Box 999, Lincoln, LN5 7PH
register of force in 7 volumes 1857-1942 (M)

Little Lever Police, Little Lever Division, Lancashire Constabulary
Lancashire County Record Office (ref PLA 50)
registers of Special Constables 1926-46.

Liverpool Women Police movement
Liverpool Record Office (code 138)
committee 1919-57: records

London, City of: Records Department, 26 Old Jewry, London EC2R 8DJ
Corporation of London Records Office (code 75)
ref Guide to the Corporation of London Record Office, 1994
registers listing every member of the force since warrant numbers were introduced on
9 April 1832, and personal files on 95% of officers who have served since that date
correspondence relating to the Whitechapel murders 1851-1947
Chief officers' files, order books, air raid reports, statements etc.
Police Reserve register 1915-18, 1921-31, 1931-40

London, Greater: Metropolitan Police ('The Met') *see* **Metropolitan Police**

Lothian and Borders Police Force
Edinburgh City Archives (code 236)
records 1805-1980 (ref Accessions to repositories 1991 ECA 176)

Macclesfield Borough Police

Cheshire Record Office (code 17)

declarations by constables as to service 1891-1945 (ref CJP 27/3/1)

police pay books 1911-47 (LBM 2515/58)

Manchester, Greater: Manchester City Police

Greater Manchester Police Museum is at Newton Street, Manchester, M1 1ES

personnel appointment ledgers 1858-1975/76

Oldham Borough police 1849-80s

Rochdale Borough police 1919-66

Salford City police 1860s-1940s

Stockport Borough Police 1967 (only); personnel files

Bolton Borough police 1920-69 (with gaps)

1900-84 (with gaps) Manchester City Police, Manchester and Salford Police, Greater Manchester Police. NOTE: there is also an unofficial index to Manchester Police officers, pre 1859 and Oldham Borough Police, 1849-59. The museum, archive and stores consist of 5,500 objects, 1000 photographs, and some 600 feet of archive material. Museum staff answer enquiries from family historians, general researchers, etc. Study space is also provided at the museum for researchers making personal visits (M)

Menai Bridge *see* **Anglesey**

Merioneth Constabulary

Area Record Office, Gwynedd, Merioneth Archives (code 220) (ref Z/H)

constables' journals, registers, photographs 1861-1959

Merseyside Police

HQ PO Box, 59 Canning Place, Liverpool L69 1JD

Southport constables' records 1933-63 (M)

Merthyr Tydfil Borough Police

Glamorgan Record Office (code 214) (ref D/D Con/MT 1-11)

correspondence, minutes, reports, records relating to crimes and personnel 1908-69

candidates' register 1921-69

sickness register 1952-69

Metropolitan Police Records ('the Met')

The original area was defined in the 1829 Act as being within a seven mile radius from Charing Cross. Within the next year, seventeen police divisions were set up, each with a code letter:

A Westminster	K West Ham
B Chelsea	L Lambeth
C Mayfair and Soho	M Southwark
D Marylebone	N Islington
E Holborn	P Peckham
F Kensington	R Greenwich
G Kings Cross	S Hampstead
H Stepney	T Hammersmith
	V Wandsworth

Further Police Divisions were created in 1865 *

W Clapham	Y Holloway
X Willesden	

*J - Bethnal Green was added in 1886

A second Metropolitan Police Act in 1839 converted the River Thames Force into the Thames Division, and extended the area covered to a fifteen mile radius. The responsibilities of the Met were far wider than this suggests, in that they included the Royal Dockyards and military stations at Portsmouth, Chatham, Devonport, Pembroke and Woolwich from 1860 to 1934 and Rosyth in Scotland from 1914 to 1926. Each division was in the charge of a superintendent, under whom were four inspectors and sixteen sergeants.

Incomplete divisional records for A, B, E, F, G, H, K, L, M, N, R and Y, are held by the Metropolitan Police Historical Museum, c/o Room 1334, New Scotland Yard. Thames Division ledgers are held at Wapping Police Station Museum.

For searches involving Metropolitan police ancestors, a wealth of information is held by the Public Record Office. As a first step use should be made of the free information sheets which detail the classes and their piece numbers. These are summarized in *Tracing your Ancestors in the Public Record Office*, (by Amanda Bevan and Andrea Duncan)

a) Registers

Public Record Office, Ruskin Avenue, Kew, Richmond, Surrey TW9 4DU
PRO Records Information Sheet (no 53) guides the researcher through the main Metropolitan Police Records (MEPO). Care needs to be taken with dates, reference and warrant numbers. An abbreviated guide, Family Fact Sheet (no 8) is designed to enable a newcomer to the PRO to find basic

Metropolitan Police records:

HO 65/26 Alphabetical Register 1829-1836

MEPO 4/333-338, Alphabetical Register of joiners 1830-April 1857 and Jul 1878-1933

MEPO 4/361-477, Certificate of Service records 1889-1909

MEPO 4/339-351, Registers of leavers 1889-Jan 1947

No records at all have survived for the years 1857-1869

b) Indexes

A private index compiled by Colin White, April Cottage, 27 Landscore, Crediton Devon EX17 3LW, covers 700 Metropolitan police officers who were killed during World War 2 and 555 who were awarded honours.

A London-wide index is in preparation by Michael Fountain, though likely to take many years to complete, extracting from the six censuses 1841-91, details of Metropolitan Police Officers serving or retired, together with their families. To date it has over 33,500 entries. This large task is supported by the friends of the Metropolitan Police Museum, but is not yet available for public enquiries. (1999)

c) Metropolitan Police Museum

A museum had been formed in 1949 by the efforts of the then Chief Superintendent, Arthur Rowlerson, of Bow Street Police Station. The museum continued until 1982/83, when the few rooms occupied were required and the collection was packed away, and has remained in store since that date. Ironically Bow Street Station was made redundant as a Police Station in 1992. 30,000 items are stored away in south London, including uniforms, medals, badges, station books and many photographs. Anyone interested in the history of the Met may join the 'Friends'. The subscription is a modest £5, renewable on the 1st January, payable to 'Metropolitan Museum Friends' at Orpington Police Station, The Walnuts, Orpington, Kent BR6 0TW.

d) Independent Researchers

The PRO maintains a list (no 17) of independent researchers who may be prepared to undertake commissions for research. However, they do not take responsibility for any arrangement made with an individual researcher. A stamped self addressed envelope (with International Reply coupons for overseas enquiries) should be enclosed with any postal enquiry.

Mid Anglia *see* **Peterborough**

Middlesbrough *see* **Teeside**

Monmouth Police Authority
personnel registers 1857-1950
see also **Griffithstown**

Montrose *see* **Angus**

National Association of Retired Police Officers
see **Gloucestershire**

Neath Borough Police
West Glamorgan Archives Service (code 216) (ref D/D Con/N)
correspondence and reports including items relating to Women's Auxiliary Police Corps 1896-1946
Police war Reserve etc. 1939-46, some files on individuals

Newport Constabulary, Monmouthshire
Gwent Record Office (code 218) (ref D/709)
occurrence books, order books, service and conduct registers, court registers, correspondence 1857-1965; and other papers including items relating to women police officers 1920-59

Norfolk Constabulary
Police Authority
appointments book 1854

Northampton Police
Police Authority
register of constables 1840-1946

Northern Constabulary
Records deposited with the Highland Council Archive (code 232) by the Chief Constable, Northern Constabulary 1858-1974, 1994-97

North Wales Police
Research enquiries referred to Clwyd County Record Office, Denbighshire (code 209). No historical documentation held

Northumbria Police
Police authority: photographic personnel register 1863-1942

Oldham Police Commissioners
Oldham Archive Service (code 758) (ref PCO)
minutes, accounts etc, but personnel registers listed for Oldham Borough Police 1827-53
register of constables 1849-61
See also **Manchester, Greater**

Oxford City Police
Oxfordshire Archives (code 160)
register of constables
private, further nineteenth and twentieth century records 1890-1968

Oxfordshire Constabulary
Oxfordshire Archives (code 160)
constables' records 1857-1957
See also **Thames Valley Police**

Peeblesshire Police
Edinburgh City Archives (code 236) (ref ED006/11)
personnel records 1858-1952
pension register 1891-1947

Penrhyndeudraeth *see* **Blaenau Ffestiniog**

Perthshire and Kinross-shire *see* **Angus**

Peterborough Combined Police Authority, Northamptonshire
Cambridgeshire County Record Office, Huntingdon (code 11)
minutes 1947-65

Peterborough City Police
Cambridgeshire County Record Office in Huntingdon (code 11)
discipline books 1874-1943
personnel 1857-1938
return of punishment book 1874-1937
register of applicants 1847-1964
Historical Note:– this police force had a 'chequered' existence, starting as two forces, one named Liberty of Peterborough Police, and the other the 'City of Peterborough Police'. The Liberty covered the Soke of Peterborough, and did not amalgamate with the city force until 1947. In 1965 the combined force became the Mid Anglia force and with local government re-organisation in 1974 became Cambridgeshire Constabulary. Records were brought together in a police station

annexe in Peterborough as a museum in 1980, and the archives were subsequently moved to Cambridgeshire County Record Office in Huntingdon (code 11)

Plympton *see* **Devon and Cornwall**

Police Federation records *see* **Swansea**

Pontefract Borough Police 1836-1889
no personnel records available

Portsmouth
Portsmouth City Museums and Record Office (code 42)
personal record volume 1937-1967, including index at front. (Closed for 70 years)
See also **Hampshire**

Preston Borough Police
Lancashire County Record Office (code 55)
list of special constables in 1826, (ref QDE 9)
examination books 1863-1968, PLA 17/18 (ref DDP acc 6318 F1-2)
service registers 1900-68 (ref PLA 51/17-18)
seniority register 1939-68 (ref PLA51/19), contains lists of personnel grouped by rank and date of joining, date of birth and a small amount of other information
Special Constables Service Register 1939-68 with index (ref PLA 51/20)
NOTE: service registers and personnel record sheets closed until 2069; the seniority register is open from 1999, but the Special Constabulary Service Register is closed until 2069. However, the arrangement described under Lancashire Constabulary may apply and should be checked first. Lancs. Constabulary PLA51
Lancashire Library: photograph of the Force in 1926 (ref DDX 15/21)

Reading Police
Berkshire Record Office (code 5)
station occurrence book 1880-98 (ref D/X 1233)
Berks Constabulary Examination Book: service record, pension etc. 1856-1929
See also **Berkshire Constabulary**

Rochdale Borough Police
Lancashire Record Office (code 55)
conduct book 1915-33 (ref PLRO box 67)
See also **Manchester, Greater**

Ross and Cromarty Constabulary
Inverness Library (code 232)
registers 1865-1966

Rotherham Police Force

Sheffield Archives (code 199)

constables' conduct book 1880-1957, (1880-1913 is not indexed)

No other records relating to the Rotherham division of West Riding Police have survived (ref 546/C)

Royal Ulster Constabulary

Royal Ulster Constabulary Museum (M) RUC Headquarters, 'Brooklyn', Knock Road, Belfast, Northern Ireland B75 6LE

microfiche copies of service records (force numbers 1001-7992) 1922-58

a number of files of officers' service records are also held. NOTE: such is the sensitivity surrounding RUC service records that they are not available for general research. Ex-force members may inspect their own records which are otherwise only available to immediate family members where a force member has been deceased for a considerable period of time

Rutland Constabulary (amalgamated with Leicestershire Constabulary in 1951)

Leicestershire Record Office (code 56) (ref Leicestershire DE/3831)

occurrence books, crime register, journals and personnel records 1857-1951

Salford City Police *see* **Manchester, Greater**

Sheffield Police

Sheffield Archives (code 199)

wages paid weekly, lists names of sergeants, policemen and watchmen 1831-1960, 1839-41

conduct and commendation books 1831-1913 (names, appointments, promotions, date of dismissals, death)

pension books 1890-1915

declarations and descriptions of constables 1891-1921 (includes previous trades, native towns and names of referees)

probationers' books 1867-1901 (giving date of application, name, age, height, address trade, married or single, number of children, general appearance, details of last employment, service in armed forces, knowledge of the Borough, friends or relatives in the force, member of sick club and pay) (ref 295/C)

City of Sheffield

Old Comrades Association

City of Sheffield Police, Force and Fire Brigade

Minutes of general and committee meetings 1928-49

Shrewsbury Borough Police
Shropshire Records and Research Centre (code 166)
discharge certificates 1905-47

Shropshire Constabulary
Shropshire Record and Research Centre (code 166)
Register of Force 1840-1909
personnel files 1875-1909
special constables 1915-1939
photographs of Chief Constables 1859-1946

Somerset Police
Police Authority
recruits declarations' books, 5 volumes 1902-62
register of testimonials, rewards to police 1904-28
discipline report book, 2 volumes 1920-1946
See also **Avon and Somerset**

Southampton City Police
Hampshire Record Office (code 41) (ref 200M86/S)
daily and general orders, watch committee minutes, Chief Constables' reports, personnel registers 1931-67

Southend County Borough
Essex Record Office, Southend branch (code 39) (ref D/BC 1/7/5/8)
constables' record book containing description and personal details 1913-36

Southport Borough Police Force
Lancashire Record Office (code 55)
Appointments book 1871-1919 (ref CBSO 1/2/1)
Declarations book 1912-44 (ref CBSO 1/2/2-3)
disciplinary book 1870-96 (CBSO 1/2/4)
conduct book 1878-96 (ref CBSO 1/2/5)
See also **Merseyside**

South Wales Constabulary, HQ (M)
The South Wales Police Museum has many records which can be used to trace family members who were in the police forces of South Wales. These are all deposited with the Glamorgan Record Office in Cardiff (code 214). Permission must be obtained from the Curator of the South Wales Police Museum, Police HQ, Cowbridge Road Bridgend CF31 3SU. The South Wales Police Force (which was

Stockport police outside Warren Street Police Station about 1900

the South Wales Constabulary until 1996), is made up of five police forces amalgamated in June 1969: Swansea Borough Police Force, Cardiff Borough (later Cardiff City), Police Force Neath Borough Police Force, Merthyr Tydfil Borough Police Force, Glamorgan Constabulary (see under individual forces). The majority of the police records are those for Glamorgan Constabulary, and were rescued from destruction in the 1950's by Mr Edward Ronald Baker. Mr Baker became Deputy Chief Constable and was also responsible for the formation of the Glamorgan (now South Wales) Police Museum.

South Yorkshire Police
no historical documentation held

Research enquiries should be directed to Sheffield Archives (code 199), or Sheffield City Libraries, Archives Division, after permission has been sought from the Police Community Affairs Dept, Snig Hill, Sheffield, South Yorkshire, S3 8LY (tel 01742-768522)

The South Yorkshire Pensions Dept (tel 01742-758575) have records of Police pensioners

See also **Barnsley, Doncaster, Rotherham, and Sheffield**

Staffordshire Constabulary
Staffordshire Record Office (code 169) (ref 3813/2)

accident returns, papers relating to war and special constables file 1914-54

staff recruits index 1842-56

personnel registers, 3 vols 1857-1963

commendations book 1859-1920

Stalybridge Police and Market Commissioners
Tameside Archive Service (code 131) (ref CA/STA)

records 1828-1958

signed declarations 1857-71

Stockport Police Department
Stockport Archives Service (code 130) (ref vol 1 B/AA/4)

accounts, information sheets etc. and microfilm of 1890-1931

record and defaulters' book (policemen's service records with biographical details, 1878-1938: indexed)

Stockport Borough Police: enrolment and record book 1890-1931 (CJP/20/10/4)

See also **Manchester,** Greater and illustration about 1900

Stow on the Wold Police Station
Gloucestershire Records Office (code 40)

superintendent's report book 1840-46

news cuttings, correspondence 1937-47 (ref D5205)

Suffolk Constabulary

see **East and West Suffolk**

Surrey Constabulary; no historical documentation held. Research enquiries to Surrey Family History Centre, Goldhawk Road, Woking (code 176)

Sussex Police Authority

East Sussex Record Office (code 179) (ref SPA, SPS)

records including photographs of groups, teams, buildings, events, activities, nineteenth and twentieth century; also copies of correspondence and reports (originals destroyed)

Personnel records retained at Malling House, SPA HQ, Lewes, E Sussex

Sutherland County Constabulary

Highland Council Archive (code 232)

constabulary record and defaulters' book 1858-1959

Swansea Borough Police

West Glamorgan Archives Service (code 216)

minutes, reports, financial and personnel records 1874-1971

minutes of Police Federation of England and Wales, minutes of Branch Boards held with Swansea Borough Police 1928-69

inspectors 1931-63, sergeants 1928-56, constables 1947-57, joint list 1964-9

See also **South Wales**

Tayside *see* **Angus**

Teeside Police, formerly Cleveland Constabulary

Teeside Archives (code 20) (MS)

register of constables 1855-1934

Thames Valley Police

HQ, Kidlington, Oxon: includes Berkshire, Oxfordshire, Buckinghamshire, Oxford City, and Reading. Training Centre and Museum at Sulhamstead, nr Reading; apply to Curator (M)

Tynemouth County Borough Constabulary

register of appointments 1861-1967

service record book 1939-67

index to personnel files 1862-1919 (arranged alphabetically 1861-67)

NOTE: access to these records requires depositor's consent

Enquiries to Northumbria Police HQ Ponteland Newcastle, NE20 0BL (ref TCBC PA/TY)

Ulster Special Constabulary, Coleraine

Public Record Office of Northern Ireland (code 255) (ref D1191)

roll books and correspondence about 1909-45

See also **Royal Ulster Constabulary**

Wakefield Borough Police

W Yorkshire Archives Service, Wakefield (code 201)

personnel register and index 1852-1913 (ref A72/166)

annotated list of officers who retired or resigned prior to amalgamation in 1968 (ref A295/22)

NOTE: the second file above is subject to 40 years' time limit

Wales, North *see* **North Wales**

Wallasey Borough

Cheshire Record Office (code 17)

pay books 1913-18, 1959-60 (ref CJP 13/1-2)

register of constables declared into office (ref CJP 13/3) 1913-41

service record (ref CJP 13/4) 1913-43

Walsall *see* **West Midlands Constabulary**

Warrington Borough Police

Cheshire Record Office (code 17)

enrolment and misconduct registers 1846-1951 (ref CJP 20/12/1-4)

Certificates of Discharge (ref CJP 20/12/5-6) 1923-69

police photograph albums (ref CJP 27/6/1-2) 1936-63

Warwickshire Constabulary

Warwickshire County Record Office (code 187)

1840 – twentieth century records

Wendover Special Constabulary

Buckinghamshire Record Office (code 8) (ref AR11/92)

register giving names of PCs with beats 1939-50

West Mercia Constabulary

Worcestershire Record Office HQ (code 45)

register of Force 1910-67

minutes, deeds, register of contracts, legal and estate papers, correspondence 1913-74

no other police personnel records noted

West Midlands Police

Museum and training centre, Edgbaston (M)

personnel records 1870-1920

index of constables 1839-90

Birmingham City Police personal files 1839-about 1955

Records before 1990 were microfilmed and are at Police HQ

Records of officers from 1955-74, who did not complete their pensionable service, are also held, as are the records of officers of the old West Midlands Constabulary, 1966-74 (Wolverhampton Dudley, and Walsall). NOTE: Records are not available if the retired officer is still living, unless he requests it. If the officer would be under 100 years old the information is available to sons and daughters, and over 100 years to any member of the family. In all cases a letter should be sent to the Curator, West Midlands Police Museum, Police Station, 641 Stratford Road, Sparkhill, Birmingham, B11 4EA.

Westminster Police

Centre for Kentish Studies (code 51)

Hanover Square District special constables, lists and correspondence 1848 (ref Sackville U2690157)

West Riding/West Yorkshire Police

West Yorkshire Archive Service, Wakefield (code 201)

register of probationary constables 1881-1977 (ref A139/22)

examination books, 21 volumes with index 1856-1913

seniority list 1891-1935

index to examinations 1856-1913

examination books (officers) (ref A295/23) 1857-99

examination books (constables) 1856-1913

list of Chief Officers and strength 1895

register of all Force members 1891

registers of war casualties 1914-22 and 1941-47

NOTE: permission to research in the above records must first be obtained from the West Yorkshire Police Community Affairs Dept, PO Box 9 Laburnum Road, Wakefield West Yorkshire WF1 3QP

West Suffolk

Suffolk Record Office, Bury St Edmunds branch (code 174)

administration, financial 1845-1966; personnel, register of officers, crime, station and licensed premises' records 1845-71, 1872-1908, 1909-37, (ref West ED 500)

West Sussex Constabulary
West Sussex Record Office (code 182) (ref WS1-6)
examination books 1857-1967 (including biographical details, and service record), 6 volumes:

1857-65	Nov 1865 - Oct 1879
Jan/Feb 1908 - Feb 1919	Feb 1919 - Nov 1927
Dec 1927 - Jun 1940	Mar 1940 - Jul 1950

NOTE: two volumes are missing for the years 1879-1908, but superannuation fund accounts from 31 March 1857 to 30 June 1906, and 1 July 1906 to 26th October 1914 may cover the gap years. Restricted access may apply up to seventy years, and permission should be sought from the Det Superintendent at Sussex Police HQ, Malling House, Lewes, East Sussex.

Wigan Borough Police Force
Lancashire Record Office (code 55)
pay books 1908-67 (ref PLWI 8-9)
appointment and sick book 1878-1915 (ref PLWI 17/1)

Wiltshire Constabulary
no historical documentation held
research enquiries are referred to County Record Office (code 190)

Winchester Police
Hampshire Record Office (code 41) (ref 200M86/W)
police staff register, defaulter book, and billeting books 1872-1909

Wokingham Police
Berkshire Record Office (code 5) (ref PS/FT/26)
miscellaneous records including details of special reserve 1914-18

Wolverhampton *see* **West Midlands**

Worcestershire Constabulary Force
Police Authority: Register of Force 1839-1967; recruitment roll 1839-1925
personnel files now computerised 1919 – present day

Yorkshire *see under* **West, South and East Yorkshire**

BIBLIOGRAPHY

Allason, Rupert, 'A History of the Metropolitan Police, Special Branch, 1883-1983' – *The Branch,* (Secker and Warburg, 1983)

Ascoli, David, *The Queen's Peace – origins and development of the Met 1829-1979,* (Hamish Hamilton, 1979)

Baines, G W, *History of the Brighton Police 1838-1967* – no date

Begg, Paul and Keith Skinner, *The Scotland Yard Files*

Bell, W M, *I beg to report – policing in Guernsey during the German Occupation,* (1995)

Bevan, Amanda and Andrea Duncan, *Tracing Your Ancestors in the Public Record Office* (5th edition PRO Publications)

Bird, Cathy, *The new register of policing research,* (Police Foundation, 1989)

Bridgeman, Ian & Clive Emsley, *Guide to sources for police history*, (Police History Society 1989)

Budworth, Geoffrey, *The River Beat – the story of London's River police since 1798,* (Historical Publications Ltd, 1997)

Clarke, A A, *Country coppers – the story of the East Riding police,* (Arton Books, Hornsea, 1993)
         The policemen of Hull, (Hutton Press, Cherry Burton, Beverley, 1992)

Doncaster County Borough Police, *A short history*, (about 1968)

Fitzhugh, Terrick, *The Dictionary of Genealogy*, (A & C Black (Publishers) Ltd. 5th edn 1998)

Herlihy, Jim, *The Royal Irish Constabulary: a short history and genealogical guide with a select list of medal awards and casualties*

Jackson, Colin, *A history of the Pontefract Borough Police,* (Wakefield, 1984)
         Wakefield Constabulary, (Wakefield, 1983)

Journal of the Police History Society, also *Newsletter*

Leeds City Police, *Leeds Police,* (1836-1974)

Lock, Joan, *Tales from Bow Street,* (Robert Hale Ltd, 1982)
         Dreadful Deeds and Awful Murders, (Robert Hale Ltd,1990)
         Scotland Yard casebook – the making of the CID 1865-1935, (Robert Hale Ltd, 1993)

Metropolitan Police, *Orders from Monday January third, 1927 to December thirtieth, 1927* (Earlier volumes held at PRO (MEP0 7) but subject to a 50-year closure)

Mortimer, Ian (ed) *Record repositories in Great Britain*, (PRO Publications, 1999)

North Riding of Yorkshire Constabulary 1856-1956, (Northallerton, 1956)

Pearl, Susan, 'The policeman', *Family Tree Magazine* (October 1990), pp 25-7

'Peeler': *The Friends of the Metropolitan Police Museum Magazine.* Issue no 1 1996 (annual); also a monthly newsletter

Pike, Michael S, *The Principles of policing,* (1985)

Police and Constabulary Almanac and Official Register for 1869, published in Manchester. (Lists Chief Constables and Chief Superintendents in Britain)

Police and Constabulary Almanac for 1938, 1940-1950

Porter, B, *The origins of the vigilant state: the London Metropolitan Police Special Branch before World War One,* (Weidenfeld and Nicholson, 1987)

Royal Irish Constabulary, List and Directory, Dublin, (John Mullany, January 1881 to 1908, with gaps). Held at SoG Library in 22 volumes

Shaw, Barry, *The history of the West Riding Constabulary,* (Tadcaster 1970)

Shorrocks, D J, Compiler *Index of Metropolitan Police Officers: warrant numbers 51530-64173 for years 1869-1879,* published 1993

Sinclair, Cecil, *Tracing Scottish local history,* (HMSO, Edinburgh 1994)

Smith, Gordon, *Bradford's Police,* (Bradford, 1974)

Waters, L A, 'Notes for family historians', *Monograph number one,* (Police History Society, 1987)